Piano Step by Step

A Series for Young and Perennially Young Pianists

Performance Pieces · Dances · Studies · Pieces for Piano Duet

An Introduction to Style

Each volume is arranged progressively ranging from easy to medium

Eine Reihe für junge und ewig junge Pianisten

Vortragsstücke · Tänze · Etüden · Vierhändiges Spiel

Einführung in den Stil

Jeder Band ist progressiv geordnet von leicht zu mittelschwer

Une série pour jeunes et éternellement jeunes pianistes

Pièces d'exécution · Danses · Ètudes · Jeu à quatre mains

Invitation au style

Chaque volume est ordonné progressivement du facile au moyen difficile

Editor of the series

Herausgeberin der Reihe

Rédactrice de la serie

Ágnes Lakos

Könemann Music Budapest

Early Dances
Alte Tänze
Danses anciennes

Compiled and edited by
Zusammengestellt und herausgegeben von
Rédigé et edité par

Ágnes Lakos

Könemann Music Budapest
K 130

INDEX
I

Allemande

W. Fr. Bach & J. S. Bach	g, BWV 836	8
J. J. Froberger	h	9
G. Fr. Händel	G, HWV 441/I	10
J. S. Bach	A, BWV 832/I	11

Courante

J. J. Froberger	G	12
D. Buxtehude	C, BuxWV 228/II	13
G. Fr. Händel	F, HWV 488	14
	G, HWV 441/III	15
D. Zipoli	g	18
J. S. Bach	G, BWV 829/III	20

Sarabande

G. Fr. Händel	d, HWV 448/IV	22
	d, HWV 448/V	23
A. Corelli	e	24
J-Fr. Dandrieu	h	25
Chr. Graupner	c	26
J. Mattheson	e	27
J. Kuhnau	h	28
L. Couperin	C	28
J. Pachelbel	fis	29
	B	30
J. Krieger	d	30
J. Kuhnau	F	31
D. Zipoli	g	32
G. Fr. Händel	e, HWV 438/II	33
J. S. Bach	B, BWV 821/IV	34

Gigue

G. Ph. Telemann	G, TWV 32:1/VI	35
D. Scarlatti	d	36
Fr. Dieupart	A	36
J-Fr. Dandrieu	h	38
D. Zipoli	g	40
J. Pachelbel	fis	42
D. Buxtehude	C, BuxWV 227/IV	42
J. Clarke	A	44
J. Mattheson	e	46
G. Fr. Händel	C, HWV 589	48

Bourrée

J. Krieger	a	49
G. Ph. Telemann	d, TWV 32:2/II	50
J. S. Bach	A, BWV 832/IV	51
Chr. Graupner	B	52
J. L. Krebs	c	53
W. Fr. Bach	h	54
J. Pachelbel	B	55
G. H. Stölzel	g	56
J. S. Bach	F, BWV 820/III	57

Gavotte

G. Ph. Telemann	F, TWV 32:4/IV	58
Chr. Graupner	G	59
J-Fr. Dandrieu	D	60
G. Fr. Händel	G, HWV 441/VI	62
J. S. Bach	g, BWV 808/IV–V	64
J-Ph. Rameau	D, d	66
J. S. Bach	G, BWV 816/IV	68

Menuet

J-B. Lully	d	69
J-Ph. Rameau	D	69
H. Purcell	a	70
J. Krieger	a	70
G. Muffat	C	71
J. Ph. Kirnberger	G	72
J. S. Bach	g, BWV 822/V,VII	72
Chr. Petzold	g, (BWV Anh. 115)	74
	G, (BWV Anh. 114)	75
J. S. Bach	d, BWV Anh. 132	76
G. Böhm	G	76
G. Fr. Händel	a, HWV 549	77
J. Mattheson	g	78
G. Ph. Telemann	B, TWV 34:8	78
J-Fr. Dandrieu	h	80
	c	81
	F	82
J-Ph. Rameau	a	82
J-Ph. Rameau	G, g	84
D. Scarlatti	C	86
G. Fr. Händel	g, HWV 453/III–IV	87
J. S. Bach	g, BWV 842	88
	c, BWV 813/V	88
	G, 843	90
W. Fr. Bach	d	92
C. Ph. E. Bach	f	93

Passepied

G. Fr. Händel	A, HWV 560	94
(Anonim)	D	94
J. L. Krebs	h	95

Hornpipe

H. Purcell	d	96
	e	96
G. Fr. Händel	d, HWV 461	97

Rigaudon

J. L. Krebs	D	98
G. Ph. Telemann	c, TWV 33:13/III	98
W. Babell	a	99
H. Purcell	C	100
G. Böhm	D	100

Loure

G. Ph. Telemann	a, TWV 32:12/III	102

Polonaise

J. S. Bach	g, BWV Anh. 119	103
C. Ph. E. Bach	g, (BWV Anh. 125)	104
J. S. Bach	F, BWV Anh. 117a	105
C. Ph. E. Bach	g, (BWV Anh. 123)	106
J. A. Hasse	G, (BWV Anh. 130)	107

Suite

G. Ph. Telemann	A, TWV 32:14	108
D. Buxtehude	C, BuxWV 226	114
G. Fr. Händel	g, HWV 451	118
	d, HWV 437	120

Menuett

L. Mozart	d	124
W. A. Mozart	F, KV 2	124
	C, KV 6	125
	G, KV 1	126
	A, KV 15	127
	D, KV 7	128
	F, KV 5	129
D. G. Türk	A	130
J. Haydn	C, Hob:IX, Nr.8/1	130
	G, Hob:IX, Nr.8/2	132
	A, Hob:IX, Nr.8/6	132
	C, Hob:IX, Nr.8/10	133

Deutsher Tanz

J. Haydn	D, Hob:IX, Nr.10/1	134
	A, Hob:IX, Nr.10/9	134
	B, Hob:IX Nr.10/5	135
	Es, Hob:IX, Nr.10/6	135

Ecossaise

L. van Beethoven	Es, WoO 83/1	136
	Es, WoO 83/2	136
	Es, WoO 83/3	137
	Es, WoO 83/4	138
	Es, WoO 83/5	138
	Es, WoO 83/6	139
	G, WoO 23	140

Walzer

L. van Beethoven	Es, WoO 84	140

Menuett

Fr. Schubert	F, D 41/1	142
	C, D 41/2	143
	B, D 41/5	144
	D, D 336	144

Ecossaise

F. Schubert	D, D 529/1	146
	D, D 529/2	146
	G, D 529/3	146
	D, D 529/4	147
	D, D 529/5	147
	D, D 529/6	147
	D, D 529/7	148
	D, D 529/8	148

Deutscher Tanz

F. Schubert	D, D 783, Op.33/5	149
	B, D 783, Op.33/6	149
	a, D 783, Op.33/10	150
	B, D 783, Op.33/7	150

Walzer

F. Schubert	As, D 365, Op.9/1	151
	As, D 365, Op.9/2	151
	As, D 365, Op.9/3	152
	G, D 145, Op.18/5	152
	h, D 145, Op.18/6	153
	F, D 969, Op.77/10	154
	C, D 969, Op.77/11	154
	C, D 779, Op.50/1	155
	C, D 779, Op.50/2	155
	G, D 779, Op.50/11	156
	D, D 779, Op.50/12	156

INDEX
II

Babell, William 99
(ca. 1690–1723)

Bach, Carl Philipp Emmanuel . . 93, 104, 106
(1714–1788)

Bach, Johann Sebastian 8, 11, 20, 34, 51, 57, 64,
(1685–1750)   68, 72, 76, 88, 90, 103, 105

Bach, Wilhelm Friedemann . . . 8, 54, 92
(1710–1784)

Beethoven, Ludwig van 136–141
(1770–1827)

Böhm, Georg 76, 100
(1661–1733)

Buxtehude, Dietrich 13, 42, 114
(1637–1707)

Clarke, Jeremiah 44
(ca. 1674–1707)

Corelli, Arcangelo 22, 24
(1653–1713)

Couperin, Louis 28
(1626–1661)

Dandrieu, Jean–François 25, 38, 60, 80, 81, 82
(1682–1738)

Dieupart, Charles 36
(ca. 1670–ca. 1740)

Froberger, Johann Jakob 9, 12
(1616–1667)

Graupner, Christoph 26, 52, 59
(1683–1760)

Hasse, Johann Adolph 107
(1699–1783)

Haydn, Joseph 130–135
(1732–1809)

Händel, Georg Friedrich 10, 14, 15, 22, 23, 33, 48,
(1685–1759)   62, 77, 87, 94, 97, 118, 120

Kirnberger, Johann Philipp 72
(1721–1783)

Krebs, Johann Ludwig 53, 95, 98
(1713–1780)

Krieger, Johann 30, 49, 70
(1652–1735)

Kuhnau, Johann 28, 31
(1660–1722)

Lully,Jean–Baptiste 69
(1632–1687)

Mattheson, Johann 27, 46, 78
(1681–1764)

Mozart, Leopold 124
(1719–1787)

Mozart, Wolfgang Amadeus . . 124–129
(1756–1791)

Muffat, Gottlieb 71
(1690–1770)

Pachelbel, Johann 29, 30, 42, 55
(1653–1706)

Petzold, Christian 74, 75
(1677–1733)

Purcell, Henry 70, 96, 100
(1659–1695)

Rameau, Jean-Philippe 66, 69, 82, 84
(1683–1764)

Scarlatti, Domenico 36, 86
(1685–1757)

Schubert, Franz 142–156
(1797–1828)

Stölzel, Gottfried Heinrich . . .56
(1690–1749)

Telemann, Georg Philippe . . .35, 50, 58, 78, 98
(1681–1767)   102,108

Türk, Daniel Gottlob 130
(1750–1813)

Zipoli, Domenico 18, 32, 40
(1688–1726)

Allemande

Wilhelm Friedemann Bach & Johann Sebastian Bach

Allemande

Johann Jakob Froberger

Allemande

Georg Friedrich Händel

Allemande

Johann Sebastian Bach

Courante

Johann Jakob Froberger

Courante

Dietrich Buxtehude

Courante

Georg Friedrich Händel

Courante

Georg Friedrich Händel

Courante

Domenico Zipoli

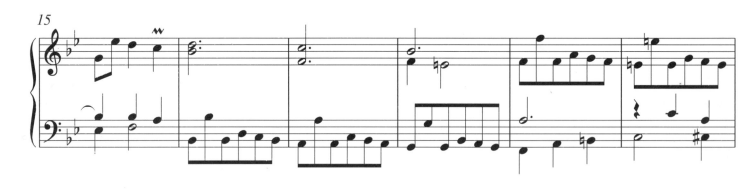

Courante

Johann Sebastian Bach

Sarabande

Arcangelo Corelli

Sarabande

Georg Friedrich Händel

Sarabande

Georg Friedrich Händel

Sarabande

Arcangelo Corelli

La Fidèle–Sarabande

Jean-François Dandrieu

Sarabande

Christoph Graupner

Sarabande

Johann Mattheson

Sarabande

Johann Kuhnau

Sarabande

Louis Couperin

Sarabande

Johann Pachelbel

Sarabande

Johann Pachelbel

Sarabande

Johann Krieger

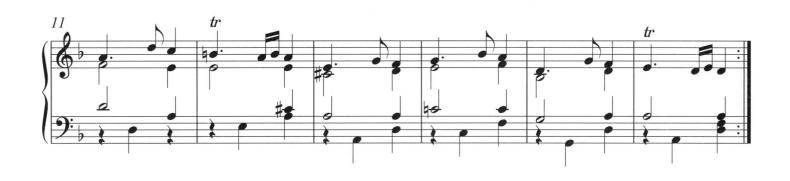

Sarabande

Johann Kuhnau

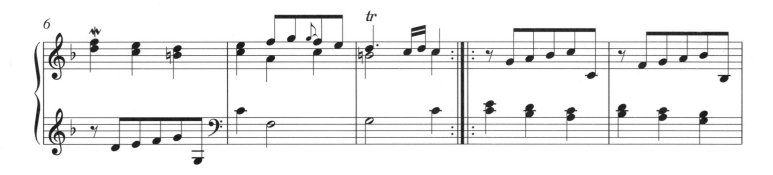

K 130

31

Sarabande

Domenico Zipoli

Sarabande

Georg Friedrich Händel

Sarabande

Johann Sebastian Bach

Gigue à l'Angloise

Georg Philipp Telemann

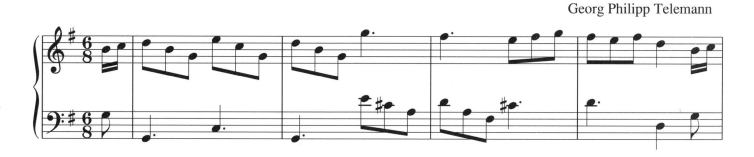

Gigue

Domenico Scarlatti

Gigue

Charles Dieupart

La Capricieuse–Gigue

Jean-François Dandrieu

Reprise

Petite Reprise

Gigue

Domenico Zipoli

Gigue

Johann Pachelbel

Gigue

Dietrich Buxtehude

Gigue

Jeremiah Clarke

Gigue

Johann Mattheson

Gigue

Georg Friedrich Händel

Bourrée

Johann Krieger

Bourrée

Georg Philipp Telemann

Bourrée

Johann Sebastian Bach

Bourrée

Christoph Graupner

Bourrée

Johann Ludwig Krebs

Bourrée

Wilhelm Friedemann Bach

Bourrée

Johann Pachelbel

Bourrée

Gottfried Heinrich Stölzel

Bourrée

Johann Sebastian Bach

Gavotte

Georg Philipp Telemann

Gavotte

Christoph Graupner

Gavotte en Rondeau

Jean-François Dandrieu

Refrain

1. Couplet

Refrain

2. Couplet

Refrain

Gavotte

Georg Friedrich Händel

Gavotte I

Johann Sebastian Bach

Gavotte II

Fine

(Gavotte I Da Capo)

Gavotte I

Jean-Philippe Rameau

Fine

Gavotte II

Da Capo

Fine

Gavotte II Da Capo

Gavotte I

Gavotte

Johann Sebastian Bach

Menuet

Jean−Baptiste Lully

Menuet

Jean−Philippe Rameau

Fine

Da Capo al Fine

Menuet

Henry Purcell

Menuet

Johann Krieger

Menuet

Gottlieb Muffat

Menuet

Johann Philipp Kirnberger

Menuet I

Johann Sebastian Bach

Fine

Menuet II

Menuet I Da Capo

Menuet

Christian Petzold

Menuet

Christian Petzold

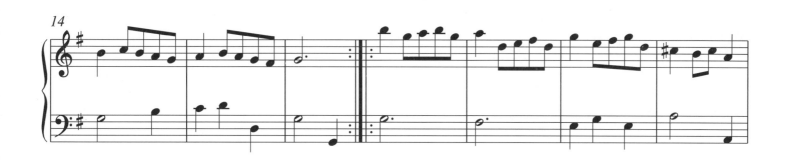

Menuet

Johann Sebastian Bach

Menuet

Georg Böhm

Menuet

Georg Friedrich Händel

Menuet

Johann Mattheson

Menuet

Georg Philipp Telemann

Le Petit Maître - Menuet

Jean-François Dandrieu

Reprise

Le Turbulent – Menuet

Jean-François Dandrieu

Reprise

Menuet

Jean-François Dandrieu

Menuet

Jean-Philippe Rameau

K 130

Menuet I

Jean-Philippe Rameau

Reprise

Fine

Menuet II

Reprise

Menuet I Da Capo al Fine

Menuet

Domenico Scarlatti

Menuet I

Georg Friedrich Händel

Fine

Menuet II

Menuet I Da Capo

Menuet

Johann Sebastian Bach

Menuet

Johann Sebastian Bach

K 130

K 130

Menuet

Johann Sebastian Bach

K 130

Menuet

Menuet

Carl Philipp Emmanuel Bach

Passepied

Georg Friedrich Händel

Passepied

Anonim

Passepied

Johann Ludwig Krebs

Hornpipe

Henry Purcell

Hornpipe

Henry Purcell

Hornpipe (Air)

Georg Friedrich Händel

Rigaudon

Johann Ludwig Krebs

Rigaudon

Georg Philipp Telemann

Rigaudon

William Babell

Rigaudon

Henry Purcell

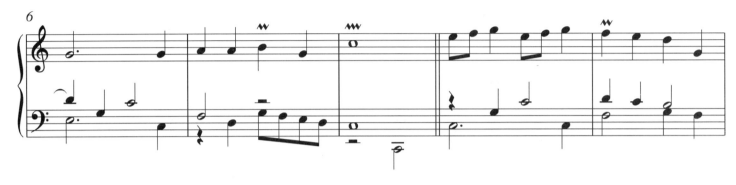

Rigaudon

Georg Böhm

100

Fine

Trio

Da Capo al Fine

K 130

Loure

Georg Philipp Telemann

Polonaise

Johann Sebastian Bach (?)

Polonaise

Carl Philipp Emmanuel Bach

Polonaise

Johann Sebastian Bach (?)

Polonaise

Carl Philipp Emmanuel Bach

Fine

Da Capo al Fine

Polonaise

Johann Adolph Hasse

Suite – Allemande

Georg Philipp Telemann

Courante

Gigue

Suite – Allemande

Dietrich Buxtehude

Courante

Sarabande I

Sarabande II

Gigue

Suite – Allemande

Georg Friedrich Händel

Courante

Suite – Allemande

Georg Friedrich Händel

Courante

Sarabande

Menuett

Leopold Mozart

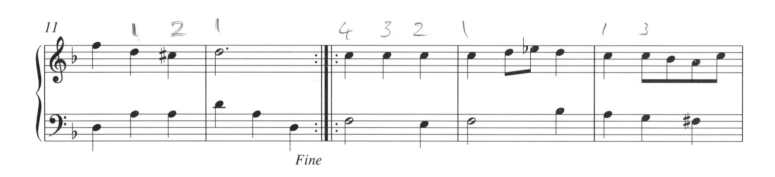

Fine

Da Capo al Fine

Menuett

Wolfgang Amadeus Mozart

124

Menuett   Wolfgang Amadeus Mozart

Menuett (I)

Wolfgang Amadeus Mozart

(Fine)

Menuett (II)

(Menuett I da Capo al Fine)

126

K 130

Menuett (I)

Wolfgang Amadeus Mozart

(Fine)

Menuett (II)

(Menuett I Da Capo al Fine)

Menuett

Wolfgang Amadeus Mozart

Menuett

Wolfgang Amadeus Mozart

Menuett

Daniel Gottlob Türk

Trio

Fine

Menuett Da Capo

Menuett

Joseph Haydn

130

K 130

Trio

Fine

Menuett Da Capo

Menuett

Joseph Haydn

Menuett

Joseph Haydn

Menuett

Joseph Haydn

Fine

Trio

Menuett Da Capo

Deutscher Tanz

Joseph Haydn

Deutscher Tanz

Joseph Haydn

Deutscher Tanz

Joseph Haydn

6 Ecossaisen

Ludwig van Beethoven

Ecossaise

Ludwig van Beethoven

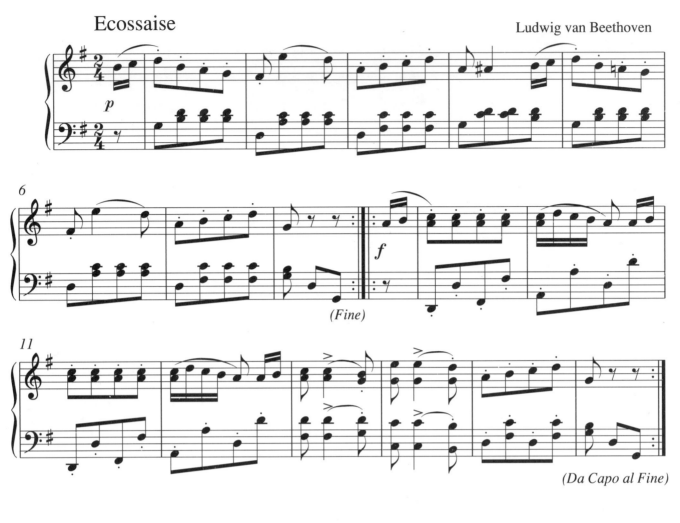

(Fine)

(Da Capo al Fine)

Walzer

Ludwig van Beethoven

Fine

Trio

Walzer Da Capo

Menuett

Trio

Menuett Da Capo

Menuett

Franz Schubert

Menuett Da Capo

Menuett

Franz Schubert

Menuett Da Capo

Menuett

Franz Schubert

Menuett Da Capo

8 Ecossaisen

Franz Schubert

Deutscher Tanz

Franz Schubert

Deutscher Tanz

Franz Schubert

Deutscher Tanz

Franz Schubert

Deutscher Tanz

Franz Schubert

mit erhobener Dämpfung

„Erste Walzer"   Franz Schubert

„Erste Walzer"–Trauerwalzer   Franz Schubert

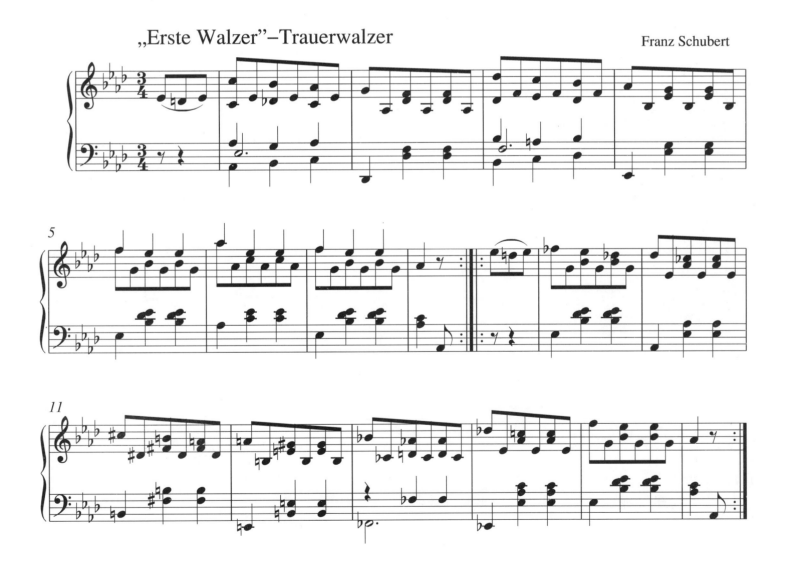

"Erste Walzer"

Franz Schubert

Walzer

Franz Schubert

Walzer

Franz Schubert

Valses nobles

Franz Schubert

Valses nobles

Franz Schubert

Valses sentimentales

Franz Schubert

Valses sentimentales

Franz Schubert

© 1994 for this edition by Könemann Music Budapest Kft.
1137 Budapest, Szent István park 3.

K 130

Distributed worldwide by
Könemann Verlagsgesellschaft mbH · Bonner Str. 126.
D-50968 Köln

Responsible co-editor: Tamás Zászkaliczky
Production: Detlev Schaper
Cover design: Peter Feierabend
Technical editor: Dezső Varga
Engraved by computer: Erika Pakó, Endre Mészáros

Printed by Dabas Printing House Co.
Printed in Hungary

ISBN 963 8303 43 3